FROM SHADOW

TO REALITY

Hebrews

by Joshua Ng

From Shadow to Reality
© Joshua Ng, 2001

Published by Matthias Media

UK distribution by:
THE GOOD BOOK COMPANY
Elm House, 37 Elm Road
New Malden, Surrey KT3 3HB
Tel: 020-8942-0880
Fax: 020-8942-0990
e-mail: admin@thegoodbook.co.uk
Website: www.thegoodbook.co.uk

ISBN 1 876326 36 0

Typesetting by Graham Wye

Contents

How to make the most of these studies

1. What is an Interactive Bible Study?

These 'interactive' Bible studies are a bit like a guided tour of a famous city. The studies will take you through Hebrews, pointing out things along the way, filling in background details, and suggesting avenues for further exploration. But there is also time for you to do some sight-seeing of your own—to wander off, have a good look for yourself, and form your own conclusions.

In other words, we have designed these studies to fall half-way between a sermon and a set of unadorned Bible study questions. We want to provide stimulation and input and point you in the right direction, while leaving you to do a lot of the exploration and discovery yourself.

We hope that these studies will stimulate lots of 'interaction'—interaction with the Bible, with the things we've written, with your own current thoughts and attitudes, with other people as you discuss them, and with God as you talk to him about it all.

2. The format

Each study contains sections of text to introduce, summarize, suggest and provoke. We've left plenty of room in the margins for you to jot comments and questions as you read. Interspersed throughout the text are three types of 'interaction', each with their own symbol:

For starters

Questions to break the ice and get you thinking.

Investigate

Questions to help you investigate key parts of the Bible.

Think it Through

Questions to help you think through the implications of your discoveries and write down your own thoughts and reactions.

When you come to one of these symbols, you'll know that it's time to do some work of your own. Each study also concludes with some suggestions for prayer.

3. Suggestions for Individual Study

- Before you begin, pray that God would open your eyes to what he is saying in Hebrews and give you the spiritual strength to do something about it. You may be spurred to pray again at the end of the study.
- Work through the study, following the directions as you go. Write in the spaces provided.
- Resist the temptation to skip over the *Think it through* sections. It is important to think about the sections of text (rather than just accepting them as true) and to ponder the implications for your life. Writing these things down is a very valuable way to get your thoughts working.
- Take what opportunities you can to talk to others about what you've learnt.

4. Suggestions for Group Study

- Much of the above applies to group study as well. The studies are suitable for structured Bible study or cell groups, as well as for more informal pairs and threesomes. Get together with a friend/s and work through them at your own pace; use them as the basis for regular Bible study with your spouse. You don't need the formal structure of a 'group' to gain maximum benefit.
- It is *vital* that group members work through the study themselves *before* the group meets. The group discussion can take place comfortably in an hour (depending on how side-tracked you get!), but only if all the members have done the work and are familiar with the material.
- Spend most of the group time discussing the 'interactive' sections—*Investigate* and *Think it through*. Reading all the text together will take too long and should be unnecessary if the group members have done their preparation. You may wish to underline and read aloud particular paragraphs or sections of text that you think are important.
- The role of the group leader is to direct the course of the discussion and to try to draw the threads together at the end. This will mean a little extra preparation—underlining important sections of text to emphasize, working out which questions are worth concentrating on, and being sure of the main thrust of the study. Leaders will also probably want to work out approximately how long they'd like to spend on each part.
- We haven't included an 'answer guide' to the questions in the studies. This is a deliberate move. We want to give you a guided tour of Hebrews, not a lecture. There is more than enough in the text we have written and the questions we have asked to point you in what we think is the right direction. The rest is up to you.

Overview: from shadow to reality

The second century heretic, Marcion, was infamous for deleting the Old Testament from his Bible. To him, the just and vengeful God of the Old Testament bore no comparison to the merciful and loving God of the New. The Old Testament had nothing worthwhile to say to Christians at all, and so Marcion simply got rid of it. He also deleted parts of the New Testament which either quoted or echoed the Old. We can imagine that he would have loved the Bible on computer–it would've made cutting and pasting so much easier!

We might regard Marcion's attitude as crude and mistaken, but many modern Christians are Marcionites in practice. They aren't really sure what to do with the Old Testament, and so they basically ignore it. A 'New Testament with Psalms' is the only Bible they need to carry with them.

For Starters

1. Have a quick glance through the letter of Hebrews. How much of Hebrews do you think would be left after Marcion's scissors had finished their snipping?

2. What can we conclude about the relevance of the Old Testament for Christians, as far as the writer of Hebrews is concerned?

3. How does this compare with your attitude to the Old Testament? Are you a Marcionite in practice? What are your main difficulties in reading the Old Testament?

The whole argument of Hebrews is founded on the truth and relevance of the Old Testament for us today. The ancient word of God still speaks (Heb 3:7); it is "living and active, sharper than any double-edged sword" (Heb 4:12). And yet for the writer of Hebrews, the Old Testament is to be read through the glasses of God's further revelation in Jesus Christ. The Old Testament is a pointer to Jesus, and can only be fully understood in his light.

In fact, the key way in which Hebrews applies the Old Testament to us, through Christ, is through the imagery of 'shadow' and 'reality'. People, objects, institutions and events spoken of in the Old Testament are but the 'shadows'; the 'realities' are found in Christ.

In Hebrews 10:1, the writer explicitly says that the Law of Moses "is only a shadow of the good things that are coming–not the realities themselves". The Law spoke of a sacrificial lamb that would take away sin. This was but a shadow (which couldn't really cleanse us from sin) pointing forward to Jesus, the real lamb who does cleanse us finally from our sin. Throughout these studies, we will see again and again how this and many other Old Testament shadows point to, and yet are surpassed by, the New Testament realities.

On the stage of God's unfolding plan, the shadow comes on the scene first. Like a scene from a Hitchcock movie, we initially only see the shadow coming around the corner. From its shape and size we know something of what to expect of the figure beyond the shadow. And yet when the figure finally emerges, we know clearly at last! Often there is a twist to the reality, a surprise. And so it is with the New Testament realities–they are even greater than the Old Testament shadows might have led us to expect.

This movement from shadows to reality, then, forms the foundation and framework on which the book of Hebrews drives home its exhortations and warnings. As we study Hebrews in detail over the following nine studies, we will see that the author uses sections of theology (or doctrine) as the basis for his practical exhortations and encouragement. These exhortations and warnings are no mere asides, but the very purpose for the book. Indeed the whole letter is described as a "word of exhortation" (Heb 13:22); that is, a homily or sermon to be read out, listened to and heeded.

Investigate

1. Quickly skim through Hebrews and note down where the theological (or doctrinal) sections are; also note down where the exhortation sections are, that give encouragement and warning.

Theology/teaching sections	Exhortation sections

As we work our way through Hebrews, we will come back to this pattern of teaching and exhortation. In fact, at the end of each study we will fill in part of a table (in the Appendix) that will build up an overall picture of the contents of the letter. The table links together the Old Testament shadow, the New Testament reality, and the exhortation that the author of Hebrews gives on this basis. (Flip over to the Appendix and take a look at the table, if you wish.)

Hopefully as you fill in the table each week, you will be able to see how the argument of Hebrews unfolds. More than that, we trust that God will speak to you directly through this first century sermon, and the Old Testament on which it is built.

Think it through

1. As you skimmed through Hebrews in this overview, what things struck you as strange or difficult to understand?

2. What do you think was the main emphasis or point of the book?

Don't ignore God's final word

For Starters

1. Have you ever heard someone say, "Well, I would be prepared to believe in God if he would just show himself to me"? How does such a person usually want God to show himself?

2. If God were an impersonal power–like 'the force' in *Star Wars*–how do you think he might show himself?

Investigate

Read Hebrews 1:1-4.

1. How has God shown himself?

2. What does this method of revelation tell us about the sort of God that God is?

3. Complete the following table about God speaking:

When?	
To whom?	
How?	

These astounding verses summarize the whole sweep of human history. They speak of how the world was created, and how it is sustained to this point. They speak of two decisive eras or periods in history. The first is what we would call the era of the Old Testament, those times "in the past" in which God spoke through prophets "at many times and in various ways" (v. 1). The second--"these last days"--refers to the final period of history, in which the author of Hebrews is writing, and in which we are still living. In "these last days" God has spoken again, but this time in a unique, decisive and final way through his Son. God did not reveal everything about himself or his plans all at once. He did so progressively, culminating in Jesus.

Investigate

1. Give some examples of how God spoke "in various ways" in the Old Testament. (To jog your memory you might consider: Num 22:26-31; Deut 4:10-13; Ezek 1:4-28, Dan 5:5-6, 22-28; 7:1)

2. The word translated 'in various ways' carries the idea of something being 'piecemeal' or 'bit by bit'. How is that contrasted with God's word in these last days?

3. Write down everything you can learn from verses 2-3 about the Son. (Some of it is unpacked in great detail in the rest of Hebrews, so don't worry if you can't explain all of it right away.) What do you learn about:

who he is

what status he has

what he has done in the past

what he still does

Verse 4 says that the Son is far superior to the angels. This superiority of the Son is then backed up by a series of quotes from the Old Testament—even when God was speaking 'in the past' through the prophets, he was pointing forward to the greatness of Jesus.

Read Hebrews 1:5-14.

4. In what ways is the Son far superior to the angels in the following verses:

   a. Hebrews 1:5-6 (quoting Ps 2:7, 2 Sam 7:14; Deut 32:43)

   b. Hebrews 1:7-12 (quoting Ps 104:4, Ps 45:6-7, Ps 102:25-27)

   c. Hebrews 1:13-14 (quoting Ps 110:1)

(You may like to look up these Old Testament verses later. You may notice that some of them seem to be different from our English Old Testaments. This is because the writer to the Hebrews was quoting from the Greek translation of the Hebrew Bible, called the 'Septuagint'.)

As modern readers we may be left a little puzzled by all this talk about angels. Why was it so important for the author to establish that the Son is superior to angels? Some commentators speculate that the original readers of Hebrews were tempted to worship angels, or that they thought that Jesus was just another angel. This may be possible, but the speculation is unnecessary. The writer goes on to explain why he has drawn such a contrast between Jesus and the angels.

Investigate

Read Hebrews 2:1-4.

1. Why was it essential to show that the Son was far superior to the angels?

2. What was the message "spoken by angels"? (See Acts 7:53 and Gal 3:19)

3. In what sense was it binding? (See, for example, Exod 20:4-5 and Exod 32:1-4, 19-28)

4. What is the message of the Son?

5. How did it come to be confirmed (literally "binding") to the writer and original readers of Hebrews?

6. Summarise what the writer is basically saying:

The Son is much greater than the angels

therefore _____ is greater than _____ and if _____

_____ then how much more _____

The practical warning of this opening section of Hebrews is simple: don't drift away. The image is of a boat which has lost its moorings. Gradually, imperceptibly, possibly without its passenger realising, it drifts away from the dock. All too soon, it is far out to sea and there is little hope of return.

Unfortunately, this is exactly how some people give up on Jesus. It was a problem for the readers of Hebrews, and it is a problem still. It isn't an overnight decision, but one month follows another, the months become years, and they gradually slip away.

However, as the writer of Hebrews emphasizes, this is not just carelessness or bad luck. It is ignoring the great salvation we have in Christ.

Think it through

1. How does this chapter's view of Jesus contrast with the way our society usually views him?

2. How would you answer a friend who says, "If only God would come and show himself to me, I would believe in him"?

3. What are some of the tell-tale signs that someone is drifting away?

4. What are the most common things that cause people to drift away from Jesus?

5. Where are the dangers for you?

6. Go to the Appendix and fill in the first section of the diagram for Hebrews 1:1-2:4.

3

The Man who rules the future

What is the future of the human race? Should we be optimistic or pessimistic? In many ways, we have reason to be both.

The last century has witnessed quite extraordinary advances in science and technology. Perhaps we will finally manage to control our world, and live sustainably in it. And yet with the technology has also come ecological disasters, two devastating world wars, and genocide on a scale unprecedented in human history. The space shuttle was a shining symbol of human achievement, until the Challenger exploded in a ball of fire.

The last century has also witnessed great advances in medicine. Antibiotics, by-pass surgery, improvements in diet–perhaps we will finally gain control of our bodies. Researchers are predicting that babies born today will routinely live to the age of 120. Yet as we find the cure for one incurable disease, several others seem to pop up. We can save premature babies who otherwise would have died, and we can abort babies who otherwise would have lived. We have cultured viruses for use in vaccines, and also for use in biological warfare.

Will mankind rule the future? What hope is there?

Our passage this week opens with this very issue. Who is it that will rule the world to come? And who is ruling the world now?

1. Who rules the world?

Investigate

Read Hebrews 2:5-10.

1. To whom has God subjected the world to come?

2. Psalm 8 plays an important part in the author's argument in Hebrews 2. Read the whole of Psalm 8. How would you summarize its teaching about mankind?

Man is...

And yet man is...

3. Come back to Hebrews 2:5-9. As the author ponders Psalm 8, what problem does he see?

4. What is his solution to that problem? What was Psalm 8 foreshadowing or looking forward to?

5. Who rules the world now?

6. Who will rule in the world to come?

There are some big ideas to wrap our minds around in this passage, spanning from the creation of this present world to the glories of the world to come. In the Garden of Eden, everything was subject to man (says Gen 1-2). God created mankind to have dominion over the world, and Psalm 8 restates this. At present, however, we do not see everything subject to man. Mankind does dominate and rule the world in one sense, and yet we don't. The world is not under our control; it frustrates us and rebels against us. And we ourselves are in slavery because of our fear of death (as Heb 2:14-15 goes on to teach).

According to the writer of Hebrews, Psalm 8 was looking forward to the answer to this dilemma. It was looking forward to Jesus, who became a man and for a little while was made lower than the angels, but has now been crowned with glory and honour through his death and resurrection. He is now the ruler of everything, as man was always meant to be.

If that were not astounding enough, there's even more. Jesus did not become the ruler of all things merely for his own sake. After all, the Son of God could have stayed in heaven and still have been God! He became lower than the angels for a particular purpose–to bring many sons to glory (v. 10). God's purpose was not just that his Son be the ruler and heir of all things (1:2), but that he should restore mankind to its rightful place as the ruler of all things. Through what Jesus did and achieved as a man, man will once more rule the world, in the world to come.

In other words, Christians are people on a journey to glory. We will one day be crowned with glory and honour, and have all things in subjection to us–in the world to come. And on our journey to that world, we have a pioneer; we have someone who has gone ahead of us and blazed a trail (the phrase "author of salvation" could well be translated "pioneer of salvation", as in some modern versions). Our Pioneer has already entered his glory and rule; and he has opened up a way that we can follow.

2. The perfect pioneer

Investigate

Read Hebrews 2:10-18.

1. How does the devil hold the power of death over mankind (see Gen 3:1-7,17-19; Rev 12:9-10)?

2. How is mankind enslaved to the devil (Jn 8:31-47; Eph 2:1-3)?

3. In order for Jesus to fulfil his task of bringing many sons to glory, what obstacles did he have to overcome?

4. How was the Son made perfect for this task?

5. Why did Jesus have to be a man in order to be the pioneer?

6. Whom does Jesus help?

Hebrews 2:10 puzzles many Christians. It seems to suggest that the Son was not initially perfect, since God had to make him perfect. The difficulty comes because we usually think of perfection in terms of morality or God-likeness. Was the Son immoral and less than God-like?! Not only does this go against our cherished theology, but more importantly, it goes against what we have learnt about the Son in Hebrews 1. The Son is nothing less than "the radiance of God's glory and the exact representation of his being" (1:3), and one who has "loved righteousness and hated wickedness" (1:9).

In what sense then, was he "imperfect"? We have been talking about the Son's task as the pioneer who brings many sons to glory. We have investigated what this task involved—nothing less than destroying the devil's death grip on mankind, freeing them from slavery to their fear of death. It was for this task that the Son was "made perfect". There was a time when he was not able to carry out this role; that is, when he was at the Father's side in eternity. We are used to the idea of people becoming qualified for a particular job. Well, Jesus had to be made perfect—qualified, adequate, complete—for this particular job as the Pioneer of salvation. He had to become a man, to become flesh and blood, and to suffer death on a cross.

The writer of Hebrews goes on to develop this theme of Jesus as our pioneer, and the journey that we are on, by focusing on another famous biblical journey: the exodus from Egypt.

3. Jesus is our Moses to the future

Investigate

Read Hebrews 3:1-6.

1. How is Jesus like Moses, yet far greater (compare Exod 3:1-10)?

2. Put yourself in the sandals of those who left Egypt under Moses' leadership. What was their hope for the future? Why would they need courage to keep going?

3. What are the implications of the important word "if" in 3:6?

In this study, we have seen that Jesus is the man who rules the future. As the true Adam (the true Man), he is the ruler of the world, both now and in the future. As Man, he is the pioneer who leads many sons to their future glory. In fact, he is liker a bigger, better Moses who leads us—the true descendants of Abraham—to a bigger, better promised land.

As 3:6 encourages us (and as we will explore further in our next study), all this is a stirring encouragement for us to persevere, and to keep hold of our confidence, our courage and our hope.

Think it through

1. What is your personal future?

    a. Are you one of those "sons" who will rule with Jesus?

    b. If not, how can you become one of Abraham's descendants who has been set free from slavery?

2. If you are one of those "sons", what will it involve for you to "fix your thoughts on Jesus" (3:1)?

3. What things distract you from holding on to your future hope?

4. In what sense are we in a far more privileged position than the Israelites in the Exodus? How is this a motivation for us to take the encouragement of 3:1 and 3:6 to heart?

5. Go to the Appendix and fill in the diagram for Hebrews 2:5-3:6.

Don't miss out

We finished our last study thinking about Moses, who led the people of Israel out of slavery in Egypt. The Israelites' dramatic escape from the armies of Pharaoh was one of the great victories of the Old Testament. God freed his people from slavery in Egypt through mighty signs and wonders, and this pointed forward to the even greater salvation that God would achieve through Christ–to free his people from slavery to Satan and fear of death.

However, the Exodus story was not only one of the greatest examples of God's salvation in the Old Testament; it was also one of the greatest tragedies. In the end, the Exodus generation missed out on the blessing of God. In this study we will first investigate what they missed out on and how they missed it, before we turn to the relevance of that for us today.

Investigate

Read Numbers 13:26-14:35.

1. How should the Israelites have responded to the spies' report, given what God had already promised, and given all the wondrous things he had done?

2. How did they in fact respond?

3. What was God's judgement upon them? What did they miss out on?

Now read Hebrews 3:7-4:1.

4. The author of Hebrews quotes Psalm 95 (which itself is about the rebellion of the Israelites against God). According to this quote, and Hebrews 3, what was the real problem with the Israelites?

5. What is the danger for us as Christians?

6. What are we urged to do about it (in 3:12,13 and 4:1)?

The rebellious generation of Israel missed out on the promised land of Canaan, that beautiful land, flowing with milk and honey. They came so close, right to its southern border. Yet they missed out, because they disobeyed God and failed to trust him. The result was forty years of wandering and death until that whole generation died. As God had sworn in his anger, "They shall never enter my rest"–that is, the land of Canaan, the promised land of God's rest.

Why then does Hebrews go on to say that "since the promise of entering his rest still stands, let us be careful that none of you be found to have fallen short of it" (Heb 4:1)? Does it mean that Christians should attempt to immigrate to modern day Israel? Should we all be joining tours of the Holy Land led by retired clergy? What exactly is this "God's rest" that we are to enter?

Investigate

Read Hebrews 4:1-13.

1. What did God rest from?

2. Thinking back to Genesis 1-3, did humanity ever share in that rest of God? What in the end stopped them from doing so?

3. How does the author of Hebrews make use of both Genesis 2:1-3 and Psalm 95 to show that there remains a future Sabbath rest for us Christians?

4. What is this future rest (see also Heb 3:1; 11:13-16; Rev 14:12-13)?

5. In what ways is our experience parallel to the Israelites of Moses' time? How ought we to be different from them?

6. What do verses 12-13 say about the place of the Old Testament in our lives?

In the fast-paced, work-obsessed world that we live in, it is hard to believe that work might not be the ultimate goal. But it wasn't for God. The creation account of Genesis 1 doesn't finish with God working, but with God resting. The seventh day of creation was a day of blessing, of rest and goodness.

Adam and Eve shared in it, in the garden that God placed them in. It was a good garden with all manner of trees for food, and rivers flowing from it bringing blessing to all the world. It was where humanity shared the blessing of good relationship with God as he walked with them in the cool of the day. But humanity lost their share in God's rest when they rebelled against God and were ejected from the Garden.

God set about rescuing humanity, especially through Abraham. Abraham's descendants, the nation of Israel, would once again have the opportunity of sharing in God's rest in the promised land of Canaan, a land of rest and blessing, flowing with milk and honey, a reminder of Eden itself. Once again, however, the promised land eluded them as they rebelled against God in the desert.

It was Moses' successor, Joshua, who led the new generation of Israelites into the promised land. Now at last, surely, they had entered God's rest and were secure! But even while they were in the promised land, King David warned them, "Today if you hear his voice, do not harden your hearts". The danger was that God would again deny them his rest if they rebelled against him. In other words, if the possibility of missing out on God's rest still existed, there must be some further rest beyond Canaan—ultimately heaven itself (this is the argument of Heb 4:1-10). This ultimate rest was not only in the future for those in David's time, it is still in the future for us.

This is why the author of Hebrews gets so excited about the word "Today" from Psalm 95. That word showed him that the danger of hard-heartedness did not end with the Exodus generation, nor with David's generation. Indeed, it is an ever-present warning, for every day is called "Today". And so Psalm 95 is what the Holy Spirit "says" (present tense) to us today.

Think it through

1. What then is to be our attitude towards God's voice, God's word? (Heb 4:12-13)

2. How are we to respond to the warning of Ps 95 (Heb 4:11; 3:12-15):

   a. individually?

   b. corporately?

3. How can sin be deceptive? How may sin's deceitfulness harden our hearts?

4. Are there particular sins that are especially deceptive and dangerous in causing people in your Christian group to fall away and miss out on entering the final rest of heaven?

5. Fill in the diagram in the Appendix for Hebrews 3:7-4:13. Do you think the writer's exhortations and warnings have become more focused since chapter 2:1-4?

5

Can a Christian fall away?

If you ever want to send sparks flying in a Bible discussion group, just raise the question: 'Can a Christian fall away?'. There will be some who answer 'No!' because after all, 'Once saved, always saved'. They will appeal to Jesus' words that no-one can snatch his sheep from his hand (Jn 10:28); or to the Apostle Paul's confidence that nothing will be able to separate us from the love of God that is in Jesus our Lord (Rom 8:39). There will be others who answer 'Yes!' because why else would Paul say, "Be careful that you don't fall" (1 Cor 10:12)? And haven't we all known people who once were with us, but now have 'fallen away'?

Hebrews 6:4-6 has become one of the key passages in this debate. It is often quoted as a proof text for the Yes case:

> It is impossible for those who have once been enlightened, who have tasted the heavenly gift, who have shared in the Holy Spirit, who have tasted the goodness of the word of God and the powers of the coming age, if they fall away, to be brought back to repentance...

Those for the No case seek other ways to explain these verses. Perhaps it is merely a hypothetical warning, "...if they fall away". Or perhaps the description of being "once enlightened" doesn't necessarily mean they were really Christians in the first place.

For Starters

1. What do you think about this issue?

2. Take a quick look at the 'Hebrews Overview' diagram in the Appendix. How would you summarize the theological framework of Hebrews so far?

The true meaning of any set of verses is heavily determined by the context in which they are located. So let's look at Hebrews 4:14-6:20, to see what the whole section is about, before we return to our vexing question.

So far, in the first four chapters of Hebrews, we have seen how the Christian life is a journey. We are those "who will inherit salvation" (1:14), for God is bringing "many sons to glory" (2:10). Indeed, Jesus is the pioneer of this salvation to which we are heading, for he has blazed a trail to heaven for us (2:10). He is our Moses, who leads us to the real promised land, the promised rest of heaven (3:1-4:13).

Just as the writer has pictured heaven using the Old Testament theme of the promised land, so he now describes heaven as "the inner sanctuary", using the Old Testament category of the tabernacle (6:19). As we will see in more detail in Study 6, the tabernacle was the tent which symbolised God's presence with his people during the exodus. He was "present" in the "inner sanctuary"; that is, the inner-most room of the tent, also called "the Most Holy Place" (9:3). With this switch in the conception of heaven from "promised land" to "inner sanctuary", there is also a development in the way the writer wants us to think about Jesus.

He is not only the Moses who leads us into the promised land, he is also the high priest who leads us into the inner sanctuary. As the high priest, he has entered there already on our behalf, and we will follow later (4:14; 6:19-20).

The author of Hebrews has already hinted at Jesus' merciful and faithful high priesthood in 2:17, but now he begins in earnest his description of Jesus as the high priest. He compares Jesus with Aaron, Moses' brother, who was the father of the Levitical line of high priests in the Old Testament.

Investigate

Read Hebrews 4:14-5:10.

1. What similarities can you see between normal human priests and Jesus:

- in their relationship to ordinary people in their weakness?

- in how they got the job?

- in their basic task?

2. What differences can you see between normal human priests and Jesus:

- in regard to their own sin?

- in regard to the priestly order they belong to?

3. In what sense did Jesus have to "learn obedience" and be "made perfect" (5:8-9)? (See also Luke 22:39-46.)

4. What was the result of the Son's willing obedience to his Father?

Think it through

1. How confident can we be of entering God's presence:

- in prayer? (cf 4:16)

- on the last day? (cf 6:19-20)

2. On what basis can we be confident?

3. Is this an incentive to sit back and relax because we are sure of what Jesus has done for us? Why or why not? What does the passage urge us to do (e.g. 4:14-16)?

Charles Wesley's hymn, "And Can It Be", echoes this confidence and assurance with which we can approach the very presence of God:

Bold I approach the eternal throne
And claim the crown through Christ my own.

Our journey to heaven is guaranteed because Jesus is our great high priest who has gone into heaven already on our behalf. His high priesthood is the basis of our confidence in the future. He is the priest–the 'go between' or mediator–between us and God. Like Aaron, Jesus can adequately represent us, because he too was chosen from among men and able to sympathise with our weaknesses. On the other hand, we also need a 'go between' who is acceptable to God. And that Jesus certainly is, for he was called and designated by God himself for the role of priest in the order of Melchizedek.

The author has more to say about Melchizedek, but he pauses, because he doesn't think his readers have what it takes to understand or accept it (5:11). And as he chides them for their immaturity, he comes to the famous warning about falling away.

Investigate

Read Hebrews 5:11-6:12.

1. Why didn't the writer think his readers had what it takes to accept the teaching about Jesus and Melchizedek?

2. His solution seems a little strange at first–to move on from the "elementary teachings" of Christ–but not when we realise that all of these elementary teachings are found in the Old Testament. That is, they are not distinctively Christian teachings, but basic or foundational teachings within Judaism itself.

Given the overall purpose of the letter, what do you think the author of Hebrews is warning his readers about? What would "falling away" mean for them?

3. What actually is "impossible" (6:4)?

4. What is the main thrust of his warning?

5. How is the warning of 6:7-8 related to the warning of 6:4-6?

6. Which of Jesus' parables does 6:7-8 remind you of?

7. How confident is the writer that his readers will actually go on to maturity? Why?

8. Why do you think he gives such stern warnings?

Now read Hebrews 6:13-20.

9. What are we to look to as the very basis of our assurance of inheriting the blessing of heaven?

As always in our Bible reading, we must be careful of imposing our questions on the text, rather than listening to the questions that the text actually addresses. The issue Hebrews addresses is not whether or not we can fall away, but whether or not someone who has fallen away can turn back. And his answer is "No"! It is impossible for them to be brought back to repentance. There is a point of no return.

It is important to notice what is meant by "falling away". It is not merely what we might call 'backsliding' as a Christian. For these Jewish Christians who had come to receive the revelation of the gospel age, namely Jesus as the Messiah and High Priest, "falling away" meant reverting to Old Testament religion. To "fall away" meant falling from the reality back to the shadow. It meant that they would ultimately be rejecting the Messiah, as their first century Jewish countrymen had done, and thus they would be "crucifying the Son of God all over again and subjecting him to public disgrace". The exact details of how they would be committing this are spelt out in chapters 7-10.

While they were in danger of falling away, of going past that point of no return, they had not yet gone that far. The writer is confident of better things in their case. Nevertheless, there was real danger, given the direction they were going, and they needed a stern warning. It's rather like telling small children not to play too close to the edge of a cliff, and yet they keep wandering closer and closer. They have not gone over the edge, but the danger is real. One way to warn them is to pick them up and dangle them over the edge so they can have a good look at the drop and the big rocks at the bottom!

It is because these Jewish Christians had not yet gone over the cliff that the warning is possible. Once they go beyond the point of no return, it is too late for warnings. Repentance is not possible.

We can't dilute the warning of this passage by saying that it is only hypothetical; that there is no real danger of them falling away. If that is the case, then the warning makes no sense. If there is a secure, two metre high, steel fence guarding the edge of the cliff, warnings are not necessary. No, in the mind of the author it is a real possibility and a real danger, and that is why the alert needs to be sounded.

So can a Christian fall away?

We began this study with the contrast between those who think Christians can fall away, and those who think that they can't. It was a contrast based on the warning passages on the one hand (Heb 6, 1 Cor 10), and the assurance passages on the other (Rom 8, John 10). However, we have found that Hebrews 6 contains both warning and assurance! How can that be? Is the writer contradicting himself? I think not.

The truth is that we have made a mistake in how we have posed the question. 'Can a Christian fall away' is a theoretical question, to be asked and answered in the abstract. The New Testament asks a far more direct and important question: 'Will *you* fall away?' It is a personal question, not some topic for academic discussion. And the answer is, 'Make sure you don't!' Both the warning and the assurance push us to the same conclusion: make sure you keep trusting God. The warnings are there to scare us about the consequences if we don't continue to trust him; the assurance passages are there to generate our continual faith, for they speak of a God who is faithful and who can keep us from falling. Either way, the message is simple: keep trusting, maintain your hope, don't give up.

The writer of Hebrews is not interested in theological 'black box' questions as to whether or not Christians can fall away. Rather, he is a pastor at heart and writes pastorally, challenging his readers to make sure they make it to the end, for God's promise is sure and Jesus has already entered the inner sanctuary as the high priest on their behalf. To reject the assurance that this high priest brings is folly in the extreme. If only they, and we, properly understood Jesus as that high priest in the order of Melchizedek, then they would come to maturity and be guarded against falling away. And to this we will turn in the next study.

Think it through

1. Do you think you need such a warning about the direction your life is going at present?

2. What evidences are there that you are soil that produces a useful crop?

3. "Genuine faith is faith that continues to the end." Comment.

4. Fill in the diagram in the Appendix for Hebrews 4:14-6:20.

5. How has our understanding of the readers' situation become more clear since Study 1?

'Mel' who?

When Christians name their babies, you get lots of Joshuas, Benjamins, Hannahs and other fine biblical names, but you don't often meet a Melchizedek.

According to Hebrews, Melchizedek was someone "without father or mother, without genealogy, without the beginning of days or end of life..." (Heb 7:3). Sounds like his parents didn't give him that name, because it seems like he didn't have any parents–which is intriguing. Was he created out of nothing? Did he simply disappear, like Enoch, who "walked with God and was no more"?

All this may be fascinating, but many of us may be asking, "So what? What's the relevance? Wouldn't it be more edifying to do a study on 'How to Make Friends' or 'Fortifying your Self-esteem'?"

We must let the Bible determine our Christian diet, rather than our 'felt needs', because all too often, our felt needs are not our real needs. It's the same with our food diet: my felt need may be for McDonalds, but that is not my real need (as my wife is always quick to point out).

What is our real need? We will return to this question at the end of this study; suffice to say that whatever it is, we need to understand Melchizedek, for it is only by Jesus being in the order of Melchizedek, that he can be the high priest who "meets our need" (Heb 7:26). Indeed, as we shall see, if the Jewish Christians to whom Hebrews was written had not come to grips with Melchizedek, they logically could not have remained as Christians! Melchizedek is not irrelevant, but indispensable for their understanding, and ours too. It is in fact the "solid food" that the writer was more than keen to dish out (Heb 5:10–6:3, 6:20).

Investigate

To understand the importance of the Melchizedek argument for these Jewish Christians, we need to understand their mindset.

There were two jobs, or positions, that were crucial to the nation of Israel in the Old Testament: that of king, and that of priest. Let's find out about them.

1. The king (look up Gen 49:8-10; Psalm 110:1-3).

    a. What tribe did he come from?

    b. What was his job?

2. The high priest (look up Num 3:5-10; Lev 16:6-10).

    a. What tribe did he come from?

    b. What was his job?

3. According to Hebrews so far, which of these positions did Jesus come to fulfil (see Heb 1:3,5,13; 2:17)?

4. Which of the twelve tribes of Israel was Jesus from (see Matt 1:1-6)?

5. Why then was it logically impossible for these Jewish Christians to remain Christians (see also Heb 7:13-14)?

We are familiar with princes or princesses having to prove their ancestry to make their claim to the throne, but in Israel of old, both king and priest needed to be from the right ancestral line. As we have seen above, Jesus was not a descendant in the line of Aaron, nor was he even of the tribe of Levi. How then could Jesus be a high priest at all... unless there was another order, another pattern of priesthood spoken of in the Old Testament? In fact, there was just such an alternative priesthood, mentioned in Psalm 110–the priesthood in the order of Melchizedek.

References to Melchizedek are extremely rare in the Bible. The author of Hebrews is the only one in the New Testament to refer to either Psalm 110:4 or Melchizedek. In many places in the New Testament, Jesus is identified as the king spoken of in Psalm 110. But our writer seizes upon Psalm 110:4 as if to say, "Look, this king whom David calls 'lord' is not just a king, not just the Messiah, but he is a priest as well!"

In the Old Testament, the only reference to Melchizedek, besides Psalm 110:4, is Genesis 14:17-20. These two little Old Testament passages are rare gems for our author, for in viewing both of them he is able to show that Jesus' priesthood is far greater than Aaron's.

Investigate

Read Hebrews 7:1-28.

1. From verses 1-10, how is Melchizedek greater than Levi?

2. Now look at verses 11-28. Fill in the following table to see all the differences between the two orders of priesthood.

	Priesthood of Levi/Aaron	Priesthood of Melchizedek
Ancestry; requirement of descent		
Relation to law		
Connection with oath		
Number of priests		
Duration and effectiveness of their work		
Sinfulness of priest		

3. How did Jesus become the high priest "in the order of Melchizedek" (6:20)?

4. What is the key achievement of his priesthood? How is Jesus' priesthood far greater than Aaron's?

Although the main thrust of this passage is clear enough, it has some perplexing details. For example, did Melchizedek really not have parents and not die? Is he God the Son making some sort of guest appearance in the Old Testament? No, all Hebrews is saying is that Genesis (a book full of genealogies) does not mention Melchizedek's ancestry or death. He comes from nowhere and then disappears from the scene just as mysteriously. The silence over his ancestry and death in Genesis fittingly sets him up as a pattern of the One to come, namely Jesus.

The second perplexing detail is the idea that Levi was "in the body of his ancestor Abraham". This is part of the collective thinking of the Old Testament worldview: you are in solidarity with your family clan, including your ancestors. Or putting it the other way, a father contains in his body all his descendants. For us Westerners, the whole idea of genetic connection from one generation to the next may help us understand it. In any case, because of this connection, since Melchizedek is greater than Abraham, he is also greater than Levi.

These puzzling details aside, the main point of our passage is very clear. Just as David foresaw a greater 'rest' than the promised land of Canaan, and looked forward to it (in Psalm 95, quoted in Hebrews 3-4), so he also envisaged a new and greater priesthood. The Levitical priesthood was still the only functioning priesthood as David penned Psalm 110, yet he speaks not of it, but of God's solemn oath about another priest in the order of Melchizedek. The very fact that this oath came after the law concerning Levitical priests, promising a completely different priesthood, meant that something was inadequate with the Levitical one. Something new and greater was required.

Thus, where the Levitical/Aaronic priests failed to meet our need, Jesus succeeds. He fulfils God's promise of the king who is also the priest, just like Melchizedek. He is the priest-king in the order of Melchizedek. He lives forever, exalted above the heavens, seated at God's right hand, thus holding his priesthood permanently. This is the one who meets our need, who makes a once-for-all sacrifice for sins, who saves eternally those who draw near to God through him.

Think it through

1. What implications does Jesus' permanent priesthood have on:

a. Whether Jesus, now in heaven, is still human (see also Heb 2:14-18)?

b. Our prayers (Heb 7:25)?

2. Jesus did not come as a social worker, a doctor, an engineer, a philosopher, or even as a sportsman. He came as a high priest. What does this say about the real need of humanity?

3. If Jesus meets our need as the high priest in the order of Melchizedek, what need do we have for human 'priests' now? Where do you see the tendency to have human priests as our intercessors and mediators in church life?

4. Fill in the 'shadow' and 'reality' sections of the diagram in the Appendix for Hebrews 7:1-10:25. (Leave room to write more after you've studied chapters 8-10, in our next study.)

7

The Obsoletor

Every now and then, something comes along which changes the whole landscape. The old ways become out-dated, irrelevant and obsolete, sometimes overnight.

One obvious example is the personal computer. Within quite a short time after the arrival of the PC, the type-writer was history–and for a very obvious reason. The PC was simply superior. The new technology made the old obsolete, and no-one would buy a type-writer today unless they were an antique collector.

Nevertheless, there is some connection, some similarity, between the type-writer and the PC. They both have the same aim (producing 'typed' documents). They have the same basic keyboard, with letters and numbers arranged in the same configuration. In fact, we might even say that the type-writer embodied the very function and pattern of a 'writing machine'. It's just that the PC does a far superior job.

That is the kind of relationship in Hebrews between the old and the new. As we saw in the overview (Study 1), and have been reminded of ever since, the old state of affairs is the "copy", the "shadow", the "pattern" of the new that was to come. The new things are "better" and "superior", because they are "the true" ones, "the realities" themselves. But it was the "shadows" that first gave the Israelites the function and pattern of what it was all about.

So let's firstly take a quick look at what these Old Testament "shadows" were, before we see how they have been superseded and transformed by the "reality" in Jesus.

Investigate

1. *Read Exodus 24:3-8.*

  a. What did it mean for the Israelites to be faithful to the covenant given to Moses at Mt Sinai?

  b. How was this covenant sealed?

2. Hebrews 9:1-10 summarizes the regulations for worship under this old covenant, including what was to happen on the annual Day of Atonement (described in detail in Leviticus 16). On the plan below:
  - label the various items mentioned in Hebrews 9:1-10
  - show the activities of the priests and high priest in the tabernacle

courtyard

curtain

altar
of burnt
offering

3. What does the whole set up of the tabernacle teach us about God, and mankind's relationship with God? What does it teach us about how we can approach God?

4. *Read Hebrews 8:1-13.*

a. What was essentially wrong with the "first covenant"?

b. How would the new covenant, promised through Jeremiah, be superior to the old?

5. *Now read Hebrews 9:1-28.*

a. What does the new covenant achieve that the old never could?

b. How is the priestly ministry of Jesus superior to the ministry of the old covenant priests with regard to:

- where it takes place?

- how often it takes place?

- the nature and quality of the sacrifice?

- what is achieved?

c. Why was blood necessary in both the old and the new covenants?

d. If the Old Testament sacrifices only cleansed the people ceremonially and outwardly, how then are they saved?

e. Imagine you had to explain what 'Jesus died for us' meant to a non-Christian. How would you do it using the categories and ideas of high priest and sacrifice?

As the high priest of the good things that have come, Jesus makes us clean before God by offering himself as the sacrificial lamb. It is by this death, this shedding of blood, that our sins are forgiven and our consciences cleansed.

Notice that what is being talked about is not feelings of guilt, but guilt itself. It is not simply a matter of feeling clean, but actually being clean before God. He is no longer angry at us and our sin, for his anger has been poured out upon the one true sacrificial lamb whose blood was shed on the cross. This high priest has done in reality what the earthly priests could only do symbolically. And because of this he has brought in the new covenant (Heb 9:15). Through him, the 'newness' of the new covenant can now be ours: now we can have God's laws written on our hearts; now we can all know God directly and have immediate access to him—all because God has forgiven our wickedness through the priestly ministry of Jesus. The new has arrived; nothing can be the same again.

As Hebrews 8-9 makes very clear, this was always God's plan. The old covenant was not meant to last forever. It was a forerunner, a shadow, a pattern. It was meant to point to Jesus. And when he came, as the new and great high priest offering the one, sufficient sacrifice for all time, he put an end to all the priestcraft of the old covenant.

He was the Obsoletor.

Think it through

1. What do you do when you are weighed down by a guilty conscience? What should you do?

2. How can you be sure that you will be saved and admitted into God's presence in heaven?

3. How is it that a cleansed conscience will enable us to serve God (Heb 9:14)? How may this be related to having God's laws written on our hearts (Heb 8:10)?

4. Are there some church practices that are still locked into the system of the old covenant?

5. Fill in more of the 'shadow' and 'reality' sections in the Appendix for Hebrews 7:1-10:25 (leave room for chapter 10!).

8

The priest who sat down

For starters

1. We have seen over the past two studies that the tabernacle, priests and sacrifices which God had commanded in the first covenant (i.e. the Law) were but a shadow, not the realities themselves. Why did God bother with the shadows at all? Why not just go straight to the reality?

Like the shadow of an approaching giant, the Old Testament shadows function as a visual aid, giving us an idea of what the realities to come would be like. They give us the outline, the shape, the categories of thought by which we understand Jesus and what he did.

In the last study, we looked at the ministry of the high priest on the Day of Atonement (Heb 9:1-10 and Lev 16), and drew out the significance of that visual aid for our understanding of Jesus. In this study, we will not only see that there is more that the Day of Atonement shadow has to teach us, but that important practical consequences follow.

Investigate

Read Hebrews 10:1-18.

1. How is the inadequacy of the Day of Atonement sacrifices seen in:

   a. how often they had to be performed?

   b. the kind of sacrifices made?

   c. the posture of the high priest?

2. What do you think "make perfect" means in Hebrews 10:1?

3. It was not only the Day of Atonement that testified to the system's inadequacy. The author of Hebrews also quotes and applies a psalm of David (Psalm 40) in verses 5-10 to back up his point.

   a. How does this quotation demonstrate that the old covenant sacrifices were not God's final solution to human sin?

   b. How is Jesus' sacrifice of himself different from the sacrifice of animals?

c. What does it mean to have been "made holy/perfect" through the sacrifice of Jesus' body (10:10,14)?

4. Look again at verses 11-18.

a. Previously in Hebrews, we have seen how Psalm 110 was significant in showing Jesus as the priest-king, who reigned with authority at God's right hand. What new significance does the author draw from this psalm (in vv. 11-13)?

b. Why then is Jesus' resurrection and exaltation at God's right hand such a source of assurance for us?

c. Look back at all the references to "once for all" (9:12,26-28; 10:2,10,14). Why is this phrase so significant?

In the Law, God required sacrifices and offerings to be made. It was his will. He wanted it. And yet he was not pleased with them, for they were powerless to do their job. His ultimate plan was to send his Son as a man with a body, and for that body to be offered in sacrifice for the sins of the world. Yet the Son was not an involuntary sacrifice, being dragged screaming and kicking to the cross. Instead, he came as a Son who willingly obeyed his Father's will. This was the reality to which the shadow sacrifices pointed.

Jesus triumphant cry from the cross–"It is finished"–signalled that his job was done. Mission complete. Jesus' death has paid the punishment for our sins in full, once for all time. As the author of

Hebrews said right at the outset, "After he had made purification for sins, he sat down at the right hand of the Majesty in heaven" (Heb 1:3; see also 1:13, 8:1). The posture of our high priest in heaven is the very evidence of this fact. He is not standing, but has sat down. The task is finished. He is a priest in heaven interceding for us, but not offering a sacrifice for us any more. His present ministry as high priest in heaven is based on his past completed work on the cross. The reality has come, and it does the job once for all time.

We have now reached the end of the theological section that spanned from Hebrews 7:1-10:18. The "therefore" of verse 19 signals the practical application of all that has been said in the previous three chapters. But this central theological section of Hebrews has gone for quite some length, and so the writer first gives a quick summary before he drives home his exhortation.

Investigate

Read Hebrews 10:19-25.

1. How do verses 19-21 (and even verses 22b and 23b) summarise chapters 7-10?

2. What three exhortations then follow? What do they mean?

   a. "Let us..." (v.22)

   b. "Let us..." (v.23)

   c. "Let us..." (vv.24-25)

3. How do these exhortations or encouragements spring from the teaching of the last three chapters?

4. How do these exhortations relate to the future?

As we think back over our earlier studies in Hebrews, the Christian life has a strong 'future focus'. We are those who will inherit salvation (1:14) and we ignore such a great salvation to our peril (2:1-3). We are the sons (i.e. heirs) whom God is bringing to glory, for Christ is the pioneer of our salvation (2:10). He has got there ahead of us, and we are yet to get there. We are like the Exodus generation, en route to our promised land, our future rest of heaven; but unlike them we are not to harden our hearts, lest we miss out as they did (Heb 3-4). We are not to fall away, but to continue in diligence to the very end so as to inherit what has been promised (6:1-12). We are the heirs who have taken hold of the hope offered to us, a future certainty, firm and secure because Jesus has gone ahead into the inner sanctuary, the very presence of God, as a high priest on our behalf (6:18-20).

The exhortation in Hebrews 10:22-25 reiterates and drives home this future orientation of the Christian life. Firstly, we are to "draw near to God with a sincere heart", as opposed to the hardened hearts of the Exodus generation. We are to draw near "in full assurance of faith". As said in 10:19, "we have confidence to enter the Most Holy Place", so let us continue in that confidence, that "full assurance of faith". For to "draw near to God" is to enter that Most Holy Place, the inner sanctuary, since that is where God is: heaven itself, the very presence of God (9:24). That is the goal; that is where we are heading, and we can be absolutely sure we will be able to enter, for Christ our high priest has already entered before us on our behalf (6:19-20).

Secondly, "to hold unswervingly to the hope we profess" looks again to that same future certainty of entering behind the curtain into the inner sanctuary (6:18-20). What we profess with our intellect and lips, we are to hold onto in the way we live.

Thirdly, we are not lone individuals as we head towards this hope of heaven, but we are to encourage one another as we see that Day of Jesus' return fast approaching (10:24-25). This care for fellow travellers has already been stressed in Hebrews 3:12-14 and 6:9-10.

Indeed the rest of the epistle spells out more explicitly what this future-oriented lifestyle is all about. It is worth noting, however, that this future orientation is based on what has already happened in the past–indeed, what has already been accomplished in the past. That is what the theological foundation (Heb 7:1-10:18) has been about: Jesus' finished work on the cross. We have moved from shadows to reality. He is our high priest in heaven who has made the sacrifice once for all time. He is not standing. He has sat down!

Think it through

Reflect again on Hebrews 10:19-25.

1. How central is Christ's finished work in your thinking? How does it affect your thinking about the future?

2. Are there any changes you need to make in your life as a result?

3. How are you obeying the exhortation of verses 24-25? What obstacles or pressures make it difficult?

4. What do you notice is different about the new covenant gathering (described in 10:24-25) when compared with the old covenant one (described throughout chapters 9-10)? How do you think this should be reflected in our church gatherings?

5. Complete the diagram in the Appendix for Hebrews 7:1-10:25.

No faith, no finish

As I write this study, we are in the grip of Olympic fever. Leaving aside local patriotism, certain events always take pride of place at the Olympics. In athletics, the 100 metres is the subject of intense interest. Who will be the fastest man and woman in the world?

However, equally prestigious is the race at the other end of the spectrum—the marathon. In this instance, fame comes not from being the fastest or highest or longest, but from being the one who endures, who perseveres, who lasts the distance. And interestingly, it is not only the medal winners that get applauded. Even as the last runner staggers into the stadium, he receives a warm welcome. He has run and finished. Some, of course, fail to finish, and for them there is no applause, no acclaim, and no reward.

The Christian life is more like a marathon than a 100-metre dash. It is about enduring; it is about keeping on going when the going is hard; it is about being determined to finish the race and claim the prize, even when that possibility seems a long way off.

So far in Hebrews, this has been a central theme. The writer has constantly urged his readers not to drift away, but to pay close attention, to make sure that they enter God's rest (unlike the disobedient Exodus generation), not to be lazy or sluggish but to remain steadfast to the end. At the close of our last study, we saw how he urged them to "hold unswervingly to the hope we profess" and to "consider how to spur one another on as the Day approaches".

In this study, we'll unpack what endurance and perseverance mean, both positively and negatively. We'll look at some of the most heart-warming encouragements in the whole Bible, and also at some of the scariest warnings.

Investigate

Read Hebrews 10:26-39.

1. What are the consequences of "shrinking back" or "sinning deliberately"?

2. What are the consequences of enduring and remaining faithful?

3. Given the context of Hebrews up to this point, what do you think it means to "sin deliberately" or "shrink back" (see esp. vv. 26 and 29; cf. Heb 9:11-14)?

4. After such a stern warning, how does the Hebrews writer give his readers positive encouragement (vv. 32-34)?

5. How does he encourage them to press on (vv. 35-39)?

Think it through

1. Why do you think people in general are not afraid of God these days?

2. Do you think Christians should be afraid of God?

3. If for these Jewish Christians "sinning deliberately" was largely about going back to Old Testament Judaism, with its high priests and sacrifices, what would be the equivalent for us?

Like a good athletics coach, the writer of Hebrews gives his readers both fearful warnings and strong encouragements. He reminds them of what he has already said—that if they turn their back on the new covenant in Christ, they have turned their back on the only sacrifice that can truly cleanse them. There's nowhere else to go. And if the old covenant Israelites were punished severely for rejecting the law of Moses (which was only a shadow), how much more will the Jewish readers of Hebrews be punished for rejecting the reality!

For us, the message is just as sobering: if we shrink back from confidence in Jesus' sacrifice alone—if we shrink back to Old Testament-style religion with its holy buildings, priests and offerings—we should be afraid, very afraid.

However, the author also reminds his readers of their great track record, as he did back in 6:9-10. It was evidence that they did have confidence in the future, for there is nothing like present sufferings and persecutions to test whether we have our treasure on earth or in heaven. Like a good coach, he urges them to keep their eyes focused on the finish line and the reward. The better and lasting possessions are just around the corner. That Day is approaching (10:25); "in just a very little while" Jesus "will come and will not delay" (10:37). It is as if you're a marathon runner, and the stadium is in sight. You've done the tough stuff; now is not the time to shrink back, but to continue in your confidence which will be richly rewarded (10:35).

But just exactly what is this confidence like? What is it confidence in? It is in this context that our writer pens his most famous chapter: the 'heroes of faith' in chapter 11.

Investigate

1. *Read Hebrews 11:1-40* and fill in the following table:

Heroes of faith	What they hoped for	How they demonstrated their faith	What was the basis of their faith	What they did not see

2. Summarise: How do these Old Testament 'heroes of faith' demonstrate that "faith is being sure of what we hope for and certain of what we do not see"?

3. When will these heroes of faith ultimately get what was promised? Why?

As these heroes show, faith is about having confidence in God's promises regarding the future, and acting upon them despite present difficulties and temptations. That is why they were all commended by God. They all knew not only that God existed, but that his promises about the future would come to pass. And these heroes kept trusting God and his promises through thick and thin.

However, these heroes of faith are more than just examples for us; they are to be examples with us. For it is only together with us that they receive their reward. Ultimately, our reward in heaven is the real reward they were looking forward to, and which they only receive together with us. In terms of Old Testament "shadows", some of them received the "shadow" that was promised (e.g. Joshua, who conquered the promised land); others didn't (e.g. Abraham, who remained an alien in the promised land). But none of them got the real rewards that those shadows pointed forward to: the better country, the city built by God, the heavenly one (11:16). And so, having been "made perfect" with us (cleansed and able to approach God because of Jesus' blood), they now finally receive what was promised. They gather with us around the heavenly Mt Zion, the spirits of righteous men made perfect (12:23).

But not only are these Old Testament heroes examples for us and with us, they are also examples surrounding us. Picking up the imagery of the marathon again, it is as if you are running into the stadium. You are tired. Your arms are feeble and your knees weak. But the sight of the finish line, less than one circuit of the stadium ahead, renews your courage. Even more than that, as you look at the crowd surrounding you at the stadium, there are all the great marathon runners of the past cheering you on—all the heroes you have looked up to since you were a child. Here then is the practical thrust of Hebrews 11: "Therefore, since we are surrounded by such a great cloud of witnesses, let us throw off everything that hinders and the sin that so easily entangles, and let us run with perseverance the race marked out for us" (Heb 12:1).

Investigate

Read Hebrews 12:1-13

1. Who is the greatest hero and example of faith? Why?

2. How is he more than just an example of faith (12:2)?

3. Why is his faith especially noteworthy given the situation the readers had experienced (cf. 10:32-34)?

4. Two popular responses when we go through hardships and persecutions are:
   - "God has lost control"
   - "God is not for us"
What does this passage say?

5. How would you summarize the nature of the Christian life from this passage?

Think it through

1. What are some of the things, though not necessarily sinful in and of themselves, that might nevertheless hinder you from finishing the race?

2. What sin can easily entangle you?

3. Pick one of the heroes in Hebrews 11 who would be especially encouraging for you, and explain why.

4. Martin Luther's famous hymn "A Safe Stronghold Our God is Still" finishes with these words:

> And though they take our life,
> Goods, honour, children, wife
> Yet is their profit small;
> These things shall vanish all
> The city of God remaineth.

Is this your attitude? How may you 'lose out' in this world's terms as you run the race?

5. How has this study strengthened your confidence in God and his promises?

6. Fill in the summary diagram in the Appendix for Hebrews 10:26-12:13.

10

True worship

For Starters

1. What words and activities come to mind when someone mentions the word 'worship'?

2. What different kinds of worship are there in the world? Why do you think they are so different?

True worship must involve worshipping the true God, the God who is actually there. We know who this God is, for as Hebrews has already told us, he has revealed himself not only in the Old Testament, but finally in his Son, Jesus Christ (Heb 1:1-3).

More than that, true worship would depend on what this God was like and how he wanted to be worshipped. Thus, idolatry in the Old Testament included not only the worship of false gods, but the false worship of Yahweh, the true God. The Golden Calf incident was a classic example. By making the calf, the Israelites were attempting to worship Yahweh, who had rescued them out of Egypt (see Ex 32:1-6). The attempt, however, was abysmal. Not only was the calf a terrible misrepresentation of what God was like, the sexual orgy that followed was not at all how God wanted to be worshipped. God was not happy, and his displeasure was rightly vented against those who worshipped falsely. Not all worship is valid, especially in the eyes of God.

Even under the 'Christian' umbrella, different people have differing ways of worshipping God. They arise out of different perceptions of who God is and how he wants us to approach him. We must make sure that our worship is true and acceptable, lest we incur his wrath. For as our passage warns us, we should "worship God acceptably with reverence and awe, for our God is a consuming fire" (Heb 12:28-29).

The overarching theme of the remainder of Hebrews is 'true worship'. There is a central section, in Hebrews 12:18-27, which outlines the basis and framework of how we are to think rightly about "true worship". This is sandwiched by two application sections, which spell out just what this true worship should look like in practice (12:14-17 and 12:28-13:21). Let's look at each of these in turn: first the right basis for thinking, then the practical application.

The basis: two mountains

Investigate

1. ***Read Hebrews 12:18-27*** and complete the table, which compares and contrasts the 'shadow' and the 'reality'.

	Shadow	Reality
Mountains		
Warnings		
Shakings		

2. On the 'reality' side of the comparison, which things have already taken place, and which things are still to come?

3. Verse 26 quotes the prophet Haggai. How did Haggai look back to the shadows, as well as forward to the reality (cf. Haggai 2:4-9, 20-22)?

So far in Hebrews we have already seen the theme of the Exodus played out (such as in chapters 3 and 4). Hebrews 12 brings another slant to this comparison. The Israelites fled Egypt in order to worship God at Mt Sinai, to gather in assembly around him and hear him speak. In much the same way, we too have been rescued in order to worship God together, to gather around a mountain and hear him speak.

Yet the mountain we have come to for worship is not Mt Sinai, but the heavenly Mt Zion. Once again, the Old Testament experience at Sinai was but a shadow and not the real thing. Indeed, the Old Testament itself confessed to this inadequacy, this time through the prophet Haggai. By saying, "Once more", Haggai not only looked back to Sinai when God had once shaken the earth, but also looked forward to a time when he would do it once more.

The extraordinary teaching of this passage is that we are already gathered spiritually in the heavenly gathering with all God's people, including those from the Old Testament—the "spirits of righteous men made perfect". Already, we hear his voice warning us about the future judgement, when the earth and the heavens will be shaken, and only what 'cannot be shaken' will remain.

We are to live now in the light of that future. To live for the things which will be destroyed in the 'shaking' is short-sighted. We have things of eternal value to live for: a kingdom that cannot be shaken.

Worship in practice

Since we have come to the heavenly Mt Zion, and to the eternal gathering of God's people around his throne, what should our lives consist of? Answer: True Worship. In the rest of this study, let's look at how the author of Hebrews wants us to worship God "acceptably, with reverence and awe".

Investigate

1. *Read Hebrews 13:1-19.*

    a. List all the words and phrases in 13:8-16 which use the language of "Old Testament worship".

    b. Now that we are in the 'reality' rather than the 'shadow', how has worship been transformed?

    c. Are Old Testament-style worship practices still acceptable to God? Why or why not?

2. Responding to God acceptably in worship affects every aspect of life. Let's look at the various practical areas that the author of Hebrews highlights.

    a. Read Hebrews 12:14-17. What does Esau missing out on the inheritance remind you of from earlier in Hebrews? What is the practical warning for us?

    b. Re-read 13:1-4. How is this different from "love" in our pagan society?

    c. Look again at 13:5-6. How is this attitude to money also very different from our pagan society?

d. Look at 13:7-9 and 13:17-19. What is the role and importance of leadership? What obligations do leaders and congregations have towards each other?

3. How is the 'doxology' which ends this letter (Heb 13:20-21) linked to this idea of pleasing and worshipping God?

4. How does this doxology also capture some of the big themes of the letter?

True worship is nothing short of pleasing God in all we do. Both our words and our actions can be spoken of as 'sacrifices' which we now offer to God (Heb 13:15-16). They are not sin offerings, for Jesus' once-for-all sacrifice was sufficient for that. Nevertheless, they are sacrifices with which God is pleased, for he wants our whole life to be lived in worship of him every minute of the day.

This is because we are already in his presence in the 'heavenly church', gathered with all God's people to worship and please him, just as Israel of old did at Sinai. Like them, we are on our way to inherit the promise—indeed, a better promise, not of this creation, but a heavenly rest, the inner sanctuary, heaven itself, the final inheritance, the city to come, the kingdom of God that will not be shaken!

Hebrews has been a 'short' letter of warnings and encouragements, as the author puts it in 13:22. It warns us against the peril of drifting away, even falling away. It encourages us to keep trusting Jesus and his death, to hang in there in the face of difficulties. How will we respond to this word of exhortation?

Think it through

1. 'Worship is more than what you do on a Sunday morning at church.' Comment.

2. In view of this study, what specific changes do you need to make in your daily worship of God?

3. Fill in the diagram in the Appendix for Hebrews 12:14-13:25.

4. Look back at the introduction to the letter in 1:1-4. How much of the content of the whole letter can you see summarized in this introduction?

5. Looking back over your summary diagram (in the Appendix), see if you can summarize in a sentence or two the flow of the whole argument of Hebrews.

6. Why is 'true worship' an apt way of ending the whole letter?

Appendix

Heb 1:1-2:4　　**Heb 2:5-3:6**　　**Heb 3:7-4:13**　　**Heb 4:14-6:**

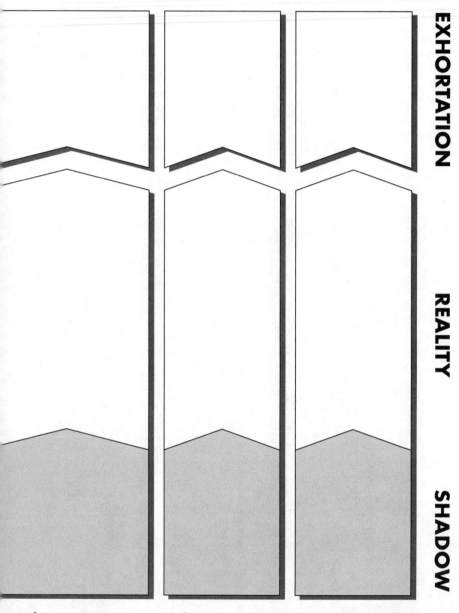

EXHORTATION

REALITY

SHADOW

Heb 7:1-10:25   **Heb 10:26-12:1**   **Heb 12:14-13:25**

Who are we?

Ever since we opened our doors in 1991 as St Matthias Press, our aim has been to provide the Christian community with products of a uniformly high standard—both in their biblical faithfulness and in the quality of the writing and production.

Now known as The Good Book Company, we have grown to become an international provider of user-friendly resources, many of them from Matthias Media in Australia, with Christians of all sorts using our Bible studies, books, Briefings, audio cassettes, videos, training courses and daily Bible reading resources.

Buy direct or from your local bookshop

You can order your resources either direct from us, or from your local Christian bookshop. There are advantages in both, but if you buy from us, you get these benefits:

- you save time—we usually despatch our orders within 24 hours of receiving them
- you save money—we have built-in discounts for bulk buying.
- you help keep us afloat—because we get more from each sale, buying from us direct helps us to invest more time and energy in providing you with the very best resources.

Please call us for a free catalogue of all our resources, including an up-to-date list of other titles in this Interactive Bible Studies series. Some details of IBS titles are contained on the following page.

020-8942-0880

Elm House, 37 Elm Road, New Malden, Surrey KT3 3HB

FAX 020-8942-0990 (pay by credit card or invoice)

Email: admin@thegoodbook.co.uk
Website: www.thegoodbook.co.uk

Interactive and Topical Bible Studies

Our Interactive Bible Studies (IBS) and Topical Bible Studies (TBS) are a valuable resource to help you keep feeding from God's Word. The IBS series works through passages and books of the Bible; the TBS series pulls together the Bible's teaching on topics, such as money or prayer. As at October 2001, the series contains the following titles:

OLD TESTAMENT

FULL OF PROMISE
(THE BIG PICTURE OF THE O.T.)
Authors: Phil Campbell
& Bryson Smith, 8 studies

BEYOND EDEN (GENESIS 1-11)
Authors: Phillip Jensen
and Tony Payne, 9 studies

THE ONE AND ONLY
(DEUTERONOMY)
Author: Bryson Smith,
8 studies

THE GOOD, THE BAD & THE UGLY (JUDGES)
Author: Mark Baddeley
10 studies

FAMINE & FORTUNE (RUTH)
Authors: Barry Webb &
David Hohne, 4 studies

THE EYE OF THE STORM (JOB)
Author: Bryson Smith,
6 studies

THE SEARCH FOR MEANING
(ECCLESIASTES)
Author: Tim McMahon,
9 studies

TWO CITIES (ISAIAH)
Authors: Andrew Reid and
Karen Morris, 9 studies

KINGDOM OF DREAMS
(DANIEL)
Authors: Andrew Reid and
Karen Morris, 8 studies

BURNING DESIRE
(OBADIAH & MALACHI)
Authors: Phillip Jensen and
Richard Pulley, 6 studies

NEW TESTAMENT

THE GOOD LIVING GUIDE
(MATTHEW 5:1-12)
Authors: Phillip Jensen
and Tony Payne, 9 studies

NEWS OF THE HOUR (MARK)
Author: Peter Bolt,
10 studies

FREE FOR ALL (GALATIANS)
Authors: Phillip Jensen
& Kel Richards, 8 studies

WALK THIS WAY (EPHESIANS)
Author: Bryson Smith,
8 studies

THE COMPLETE CHRISTIAN
(COLOSSIANS)
Authors: Phillip Jensen
and Tony Payne, 8 studies

ALL LIFE IS HERE (1 TIM)
Authors: Phillip Jensen
and Greg Clarke, 9 studies

RUN THE RACE (2 TIM)
Author: Bryson Smith,
6 studies

THE PATH TO GODLINESS
(TITUS)
Authors: Phillip Jensen
and Tony Payne, 6 studies

FROM SHADOW TO REALITY
(HEBREWS)
Author: Joshua Ng,
10 studies

THE IMPLANTED WORD
(JAMES)
Authors: Phillip Jensen
and K.R. Birkett, 8 studies

HOMEWARD BOUND (1 PETER)
Authors: Phillip Jensen and
Tony Payne, 10 studies

ALL YOU NEED TO KNOW
(2 PETER)
Author: Bryson Smith,
6 studies

TOPICAL BIBLE STUDIES

BOLD I APPROACH
(PRAYER)
Author: Tony Payne,
6 studies

CASH VALUES
(MONEY)
Author: Tony Payne,
5 studies

THE BLUEPRINT
(DOCTRINE)
Authors: Phillip Jensen
& Tony Payne, 11 studies

WOMAN OF GOD
Author: Terry Blowes
8 studies

THE MAN WHO MAKES A DIFFERENCE (EPHESIANS)
Author: Tony Payne
7 studies
This set of studies from Ephesians, is designed especially for men, and is sold as a separate leaders' guide and study guide

For an up-to date list visit:
www.thegoodbook.co.uk
or call 020-8942-0880